Maths Adventure Stories

The Mystery of the Division Dragon

Solve the puzzles, save the world!

ARCTURUS

This edition published in 2020 by Arcturus Publishing Limited
26/27 Bickels Yard, 151–153 Bermondsey Street,
London SE1 3HA

Author: William Potter
Illustrator: Rayanne Vieira
Editors: Sebastian Rydberg, Joe Harris, and Julia Adams
Designers: Amy McSimpson and Elaine Wilkinson

ISBN: 978-1-83940-324-8
CH008096NT
Supplier 33, Date 0220, Print run 9660

Printed in China

What is STEM?

STEM is a world-wide initiative that aims to cultivate an interest in Science, Technology, Engineering, and Mathematics, in an effort to promote these disciplines to as wide a variety of students as possible.

HOW TO USE THIS BOOK

This exciting, interactive adventure story features puzzles on every page. When you reach a puzzle, stop! You must "unlock" the next part of story by solving that problem. Don't skip ahead until you've worked out the answer! Check that your solution is correct by turning to the back of the book.

It's worth having some scrap paper handy for any working out. Give each puzzle your best shot, and don't worry if you get some answers wrong first time—you can still carry on with the story and try again later.

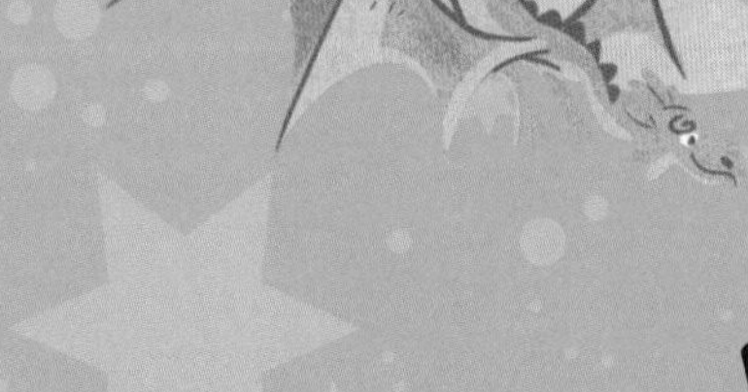

HAPPY ADVENTURING!

Meet Anna Kadabra and Cleo

When precious items go missing from the Mathmagical Museum, you need someone with special skills to find the culprit. Here is the best team for the job.

Anna Kadabra

Anna Kadabra is the country's leading wizard detective. Her special skills are mathmagic and number charms. She has used her working-out wand and the Arithmetic Amulet to successfully solve many calculated crimes.

Cleo

Cleo is a young sphinx who has been turned to stone to guard the magical relics of the Egyptian Pharaohs. She comes back to life to help Anna in her investigations.

It's after hours at the Mathmagical Museum. The visitors are gone, and the lights are low. Everything is quiet, but something extraordinary is flying across the hall. A little green dragon uses its flaming breath to disable the Charm Alarm security system and enter Room 23.

3	4	5	6
x4	+10	x4	-4
+3	÷2	-2	x11
÷3	x3	÷6	+8
x6	-5	+20	÷5

6	30	16	23

The dragon has burned through the Charm Alarm wires. Can you repair them by matching each vertical sequence to the correct number at the bottom? Start with each top number and work your way down the wire to solve the equations using your notepad.

Room 23 is the Chamber of Ancient Egyptian Magic, where Cleo the little sphinx stands guard. The dragon slips in unnoticed, and casts a spell to open the sarcophagus.

ANUBIS 81

64 30 6 7 5 16 49 36 4 48 8 9 25 24

Can you wake Cleo from her ancient slumber, to stop this sneaky dragon? Match six numbers in the room with their squares to bring her back to life. For example, $4^2 = 16$.

With the awakening spell unlocked, Cleo comes to life. She purrs as she opens her eyes, but then growls when she spots the dragon disappearing into the sarcophagus.

In the sarcophagus is the mummy of Thetsukah. On his head is a gold headdress covered with glittering gems, including the sacred pink scarab gem!

To remove the headdress, the dragon must press the one gem on the headdress without a line of symmetry. Which one is it?

With the headdress in his jaws, the dragon flies away in haste. Cleo gives chase, and the pair hurl simple mathmagical spells to slow each other down.

Meooowrrr!

0.5
1.75
1.25
0.25
0.6
0.1
1.5
0.7

$\frac{3}{5}$ $\frac{1}{4}$ $\frac{5}{4}$ $\frac{1}{10}$ $\frac{1}{2}$ $\frac{1}{10}$ $\frac{1}{4}$ $\frac{3}{2}$

The dragon stops, rips the pink ruby from the headdress with its claws, and drops it through a grille in the floor. Can Cleo stop the dragon escaping this way too?

The green dragon is launching decimals at Cleo. Help her fight back by matching the decimal numbers with her fractions.

The next morning, the museum's security guard has called in mathmagical detective Anna Kadabra to help. "Another stolen gem!" says Anna. "That's the eighth this month! Did you say a dragon escaped with the pink gem down this grille?"

"That's what the Charm Alarm security camera shows," says the guard. "That baby sphinx tried to squeeze in after the dragon, but it got stuck. That's where I found her this morning."

To make Anna's translation spell begin, work out what numbers the letters A, B, and C equal in this set of equations:

$$A + B = 10$$
$$C - A = 5$$
$$12 - B = 6$$

With the translation spell working, Anna talks to Cleo, not in Ancient Egyptian, but in Ancient Cat!

"My name is Cleo, and I'm not a baby sphinx!" Cleo insists. "I am thousands of years old!"

"Nice to meet you, Cleo," says Anna. "I'm Anna, the Mathmagic detective. Were you trying to catch the thief?"

"That's my job," says Cleo. "I was turned to stone over 2,000 years ago, to guard over Pharaoh Thetsukah's tomb, but not only have I been unable to protect it, I've now lost his sacred scarab gem!" she sobs.

"Don't feel bad, Cleo," says Anna. "Together, I'm sure we can put things right. Why do you think the dragon went after this specific object?"

"It's not the first magical gem to disappear," says the security guard.

The guard shows Anna and Cleo a picture of the other gems stolen. They form a pattern. What would the next two gems be in the sequence?

Anna rubs her amulet. Aha! It shows her that the gems are in the museum, but not exactly where.

MAP ROOM KEY

"They're not in the collection," says the guard. "They must be in one of the museum's secret rooms."

"Secret rooms?" says Cleo. "How typical of a magic museum to have rooms that no one can find!"

"To find a secret room, we need a map!" cries Anna.

"I know where to find that," says Cleo with a smile, "The map room! Look, there is the key."

To release the key, they need to complete the number tiles on the pyramid below. Adding two tiles together equals the number on the tile above them. Copy the pyramid to your notepad and fill in the gaps to work out the numbers to the top.

Having worked out the missing numbers, the key magically appears in Anna's hand. Cleo takes her to the map room, and Anna opens the door. The room is full of ancient atlases and guide books to forgotten places. Curiously, there are several books with numbers on the spines. Suddenly, they hear a voice ...

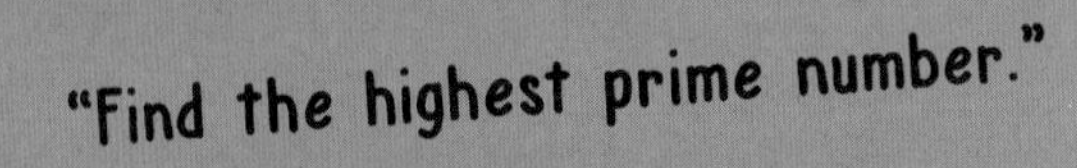

It feels like we're following a trail! Which book has the highest prime number?

25
27
15
17
35
23
7
33

As Anna pulls the correct book from the shelf, a tiny, white dragon leaps from the top of the bookcase. It must have been his voice that they heard! Cleo yelps with surprise. The dragon tries to look as fierce as possible.

I am the custodian of the maps, and no one can read these magical tomes without first solving my riddle!

At first, I am 104. Halve me, halve me, and halve me again. What have I become?

When Anna answers correctly, the tiny dragon flaps back to the top of the bookcase and allows the pair to open the book. "Look, Cleo," says Anna, "There's a map tucked between the pages!" The map shows numbered hidden rooms in the Mathmagical Museum.

64
36
81
49
25
16
32
9
4
1

Only one of the rooms is not a square number. Which one?

Anna and Cleo decide they must go to that room. Before they leave, the white dragon says, “To find what you seek, you will need to look high, not low!” Then it disappears.
“I don’t trust dragons,” says Cleo, “but that one has been quite helpful.”
They head toward the secret room. Anna waves her wand at a wall where the door to the secret room should be. She casts a spell:
“Unseen by mere mortal, reveal the magic portal!”
In a puff of magic, a stone doorway appears revealing a large stone circle.

Are we still in the museum?

The dragon said to look high. Which stone is the tallest?

It’s not the tallest stone we’re looking for, Cleo. It’s the highest number!

As Anna is quick to realize, the standing stones are positioned as Roman numerals. Which stones represent the highest number?

The pair look closely at one of the stones. There are mysterious symbols carved into the surface. "It looks as if we need to match them up," says Anna. "But what happens if we do?" Cleo wonders aloud. She's starting to get nervous, but it's her job to get that gem back.

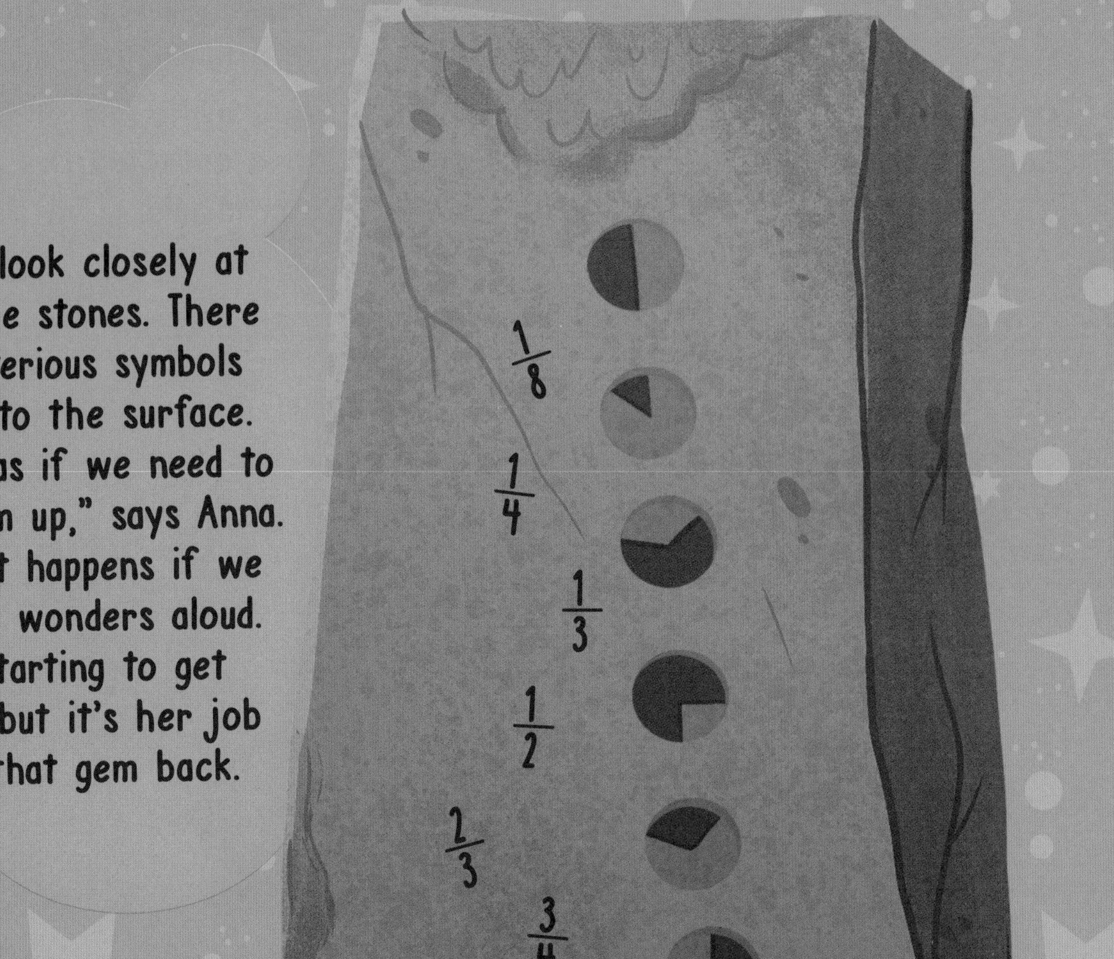

$\frac{1}{8}$ $\frac{1}{4}$ $\frac{1}{3}$ $\frac{1}{2}$ $\frac{2}{3}$ $\frac{3}{4}$

The dark shapes on the stone are all fractions. Copy the fractions and the shapes to your notepad and match them up to free the spirit of the rocks.

As the last two fractions are matched, the ground beneath Anna's feet begins to tremble, and the stone turns into a huge rock monster. "Do you think he's friendly?" wonders Cleo. In answer, the monster starts to throw numbered rocks at Anna and Cleo. "YOU NOT STEAL GEM!" bellows the creature.

Anna knows how to divide up the rocks to destroy them. She fires a stream of numbers at them, each a factor of one of the monster's numbers. Using your notepad, match the numbers coming from her wand with the rocks. For example, 16 can be exactly divided by 4.

The last rock turns into a blue gem, but as it falls to the ground, it is snatched up by a little blue dragon, who then disappears.

Anna and Cleo race back to the map room. The white dragon is still there, calmly guarding the books.
Cleo gives the dragon a hard stare. "Why did you send us to that dangerous place? I knew we shouldn't have trusted you!"
"The map reveals what it wants to reveal. I have no control over it," replies the dragon. "Perhaps it's showing you where the next theft will happen." Anna consults the map again, and the dragon is right! It now shows two paths to different rooms.

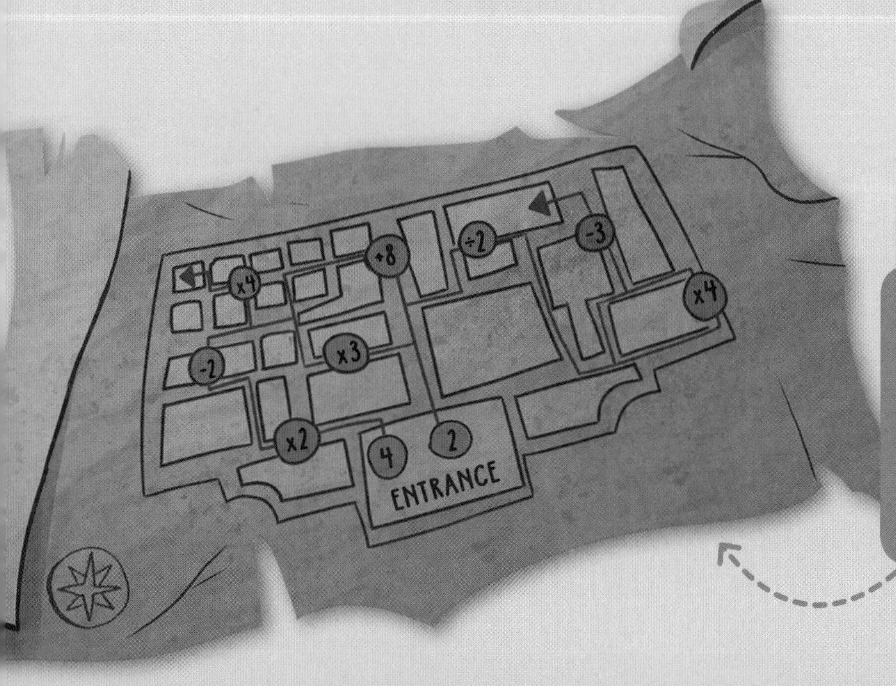

"Look, Cleo," says Anna. "Which path should we take?"

Without using the same path more than once, trace the route with your finger that adds up to the highest number.

Anna and Cleo follow the route. It leads them up a long staircase to a door that is frozen shut. Anna uses a warming spell to thaw the ice. When the door opens, they are shocked to see a mountain path that leads up to an abandoned temple.

That must be where the gem thief is headed next!

I don't like heights, and I'm not keen on the cold either!

When they get to the temple, the door is padlocked. There is a set of instructions. Which number will the dial point to when the moves are completed?

12
3
6
9

Turn me 45° as the clock moves, 180° the opposite way, 450 as the clock moves, 90° the opposite way, 180° as the clock moves, 90° as the clock moves.

Inside, the temple is lit by yak-butter candles. It's not abandoned after all! Shivering, Cleo sees a table covered in white fur, and a goblet with a glowing yellow gem on the top. Anna quickly casts a spell upon it. She's not going to lose this one!

Suddenly, there is a roar, and a huge white yeti appears in the doorway.

80.75 6^2 30

8^2 5.4 $5\frac{1}{4}$

$80\frac{1}{2}$ 4^2 15

$\frac{1}{4}$ 0.5

Help Anna cast a weather spell to blow the yeti back outside. Her wand produces a whirlwind of numbers, but they need to be put in order—from low to high. Can you help?

Anna succeeds in sending the yeti away in a blast of wind, but when she turns around, she sees the yellow gem has gone! Cleo is frustrated. "What a useless guardian I am!" she cries. Anna tells her not to worry. "The spell I cast on the gem was a tracking charm. My amulet will lead us to the thief's whereabouts."

9 11 13 16 17 21 23 25 28 35 36 37 43 48 49 64

To activate the tracking charm, Anna needs to choose the right number from the ring floating around the goblet. Copy the numbers to your notepad and remove all the multiples of 7, all the square numbers, and all the prime numbers. What is left?

The amulet leads the detectives back through the museum, and down to the basement. There are two tunnels to choose from. Eager to prove herself, Cleo races along one toward a light, but Anna's amulet tells her to go down the other tunnel. Reluctantly, she follows Cleo, but the path splits and splits again. It's easy to get lost, and Cleo is nowhere to be seen!

To find her way back, Anna needs a backward mathmagical spell. Work out what number she began with in this equation: $? \times 2 + 2 - 3 = 19$.

Back where they started, Anna takes the correct tunnel to follow the stolen gem. She uses her wand to light the way, but fails to notice a trapdoor. Suddenly, she finds herself falling, and lands, slightly bruised, in a secret cellar. The room is lit by a glowing light from a pile of gems. She's found them!

Anna's amulet senses another presence in the room. "Who's there?" she calls. Perhaps she can use one of the gems to cast a revealing spell. The gem she needs has a number that is made by multiplying together the numbers on two other gems. Can you see it?

3 6 9 12 16 24 26 29 32 40 42 38 48 55

As she reaches to pick it up, an enormous dragon reveals itself. "Thank you," it says. "Without you and your sphinx, I would never have been able to collect those last two gems!" The dragon steps aside to reveal the tiny sphinx imprisoned in a cage.
"Cleo!" cries Anna. "So, all those little dragons were working for you!" she says to the giant monster.
The dragon laughs. "Working for me? They are all part of me!"

"Let me out, you thieving dragon!" demands Cleo. Anna raises her wand to free Cleo, but the huge dragon is too strong for her magic.

Without warning, the dragon breathes a jet of fire! Can you help Anna to turn away the flames, by completing these division equations?

44 ÷ ? = 4
48 ÷ ? = 6
35 ÷ ? = 5

27 ÷ ? = 9
42 ÷ ? = 7
36 ÷ ? = 3

"Your mathmagic won't protect you, little one," grins the giant creature. "Don't you like my gem collection? It lights up my lair."

"I don't like thieves!" says brave Anna. "Especially big monster thieves!"

"I am not a monster," says the dragon. "I will strike you a deal. If you can solve this puzzle, I shall let you live."

Look at this collection of gems. Find one with more than four sides and fewer than eight. It must touch more than two gems but not one with eight sides.

When Anna chooses the correct gem, the dragon simply smiles.
"Two lives, two puzzles, or have you forgotten little Cleo?"
The dragon sets another number puzzle.

You meanie!

Look at the 60 jewels on the dragon's wing. What percentage of them are blue? What percentage are pink? What percentage are oval? Work out the answers to save Cleo.

Anna gets it right again, and the dragon agrees to let them live, but says they can never leave his dark cellar! "I cannot have you telling anyone about these gems," it says. "They are all that light my lonely prison."

"Prison?" asks Anna. "But can't you divide and escape as smaller dragons anytime you want?"

"Alas, no. I can only free one part of myself at a time. I was trapped here in the darkness thousands of years ago by a wizard. That's why I collect the gems."

"What if I could promise you a light that is brighter than all your gems put together?" asks Anna.

"If you could bring me that, of course I would free you," said the dragon.

To deliver on that promise, Anna works out how bright all of the dragon's gems are. 30% of the light in the cellar is produced by 60 pink gems, 25% by 100 blue gems, 20% by 80 yellow gems, and the rest by 250 other gems. What percentage of the light is produced by each kind of gem?

Anna's spell creates a hole in the ceiling that lets a stream of bright sunlight into the cellar. The light reflects off the gems, temporarily blinding the dragon, and allowing Anna to free Cleo. But the dragon's reaction is a surprise to Anna. Tears spring to its eyes.

"Thank you," it says. "I have spent so long trapped in the dark trying to bring a little light to it, I had forgotten the beauty of sunlight."

"Anna?" cautions Cleo. "You're not thinking of freeing this huge, thieving dragon, are you?" The dragon overhears her.

"All I want," sighs the dragon, "is to live peacefully, and watch the sun rise every morning. I'll give back all the magical gems for that."

To avoid any magical accidents, the gems must be collected into groups that add up to 50, before they are returned to the museum. Triangular gems equal 20, square 10, circular 5, and heart-shaped 2. Each group must have at least one of each kind of gem. What combination of gems should each group have?

Once the dragon is freed, Anna finds a home for it in a cave on a high mountain, where it can watch the sunrise every day. Back in the museum, the stolen gems have been returned, and Cleo is asked whether or not she will return to being a stone guardian. "I've been doing that job for over 2,000 years," she claims, "and I wasn't really that good at it!"

Anna agrees to train Cleo as her mathmagical assistant and new adventures await!

Cleo chooses a magic wand to begin her mathmagical training. Each has a number. The number of the wand she chooses is exactly divisible by 3, and it can be found by taking away one wand number from another. Which is it?

ANSWERS

PAGE 5

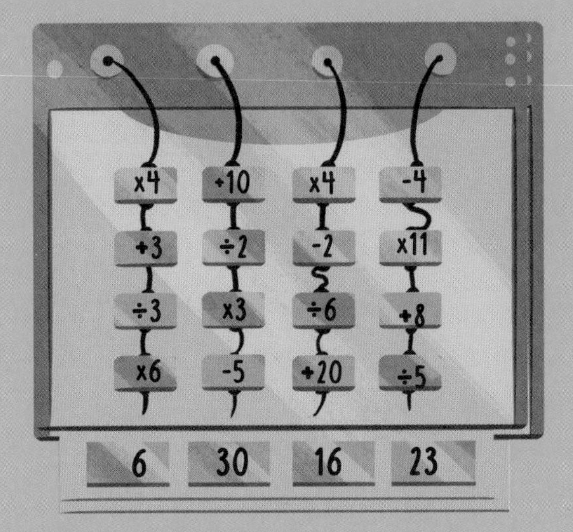

Wire 3 x 4 + 3 ÷ 3 x 6 = 30
Wire 4 + 10 ÷ 2 x 3 - 5 = 16
Wire 5 x 4 - 2 ÷ 6 + 20 = 23
Wire 6 - 4 x 11 + 8 ÷ 5 = 6

PAGE 6

$4^2 = 16$, $5^2 = 25$, $6^2 = 36$, $7^2 = 49$, $8^2 = 64$, $9^2 = 81$.

PAGE 7

This blue gem on the left is the only one without a line of symmetry.

PAGE 8

$0.1 = \frac{1}{10}$, $0.25 = \frac{1}{4}$, $0.5 = \frac{1}{2}$, $0.6 = \frac{3}{5}$, $0.7 = \frac{7}{10}$, $1.25 = \frac{5}{4}$, $1.5 = \frac{3}{2}$, $1.75 = \frac{7}{4}$.

PAGE 9

A = 4, B = 6, C = 9.

PAGE 10

The gems are in the order yellow, pink, blue, with the number of sides decreasing by one each time, so the next two gems will be yellow and three-sided.

PAGE 11

PAGE 12

The highest prime number is 23.

PAGE 13

The dragon's riddle: 13
32 is not a square number.

PAGE 14

XI for 11

PAGE 15

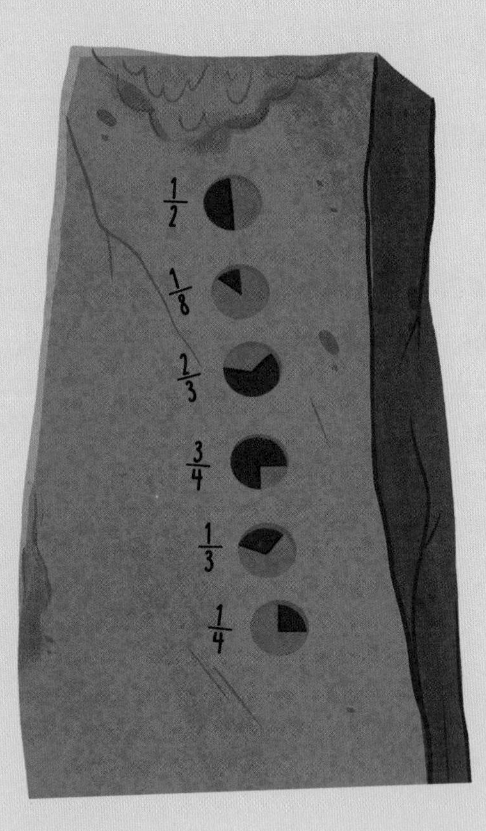

PAGE 16

12 can be exactly divided by 6, 14 by 7, 15 by 5, 27 by 9, 32 by 8, 33 by 11.

PAGE 17

The white route adds up to the highest number: 25.

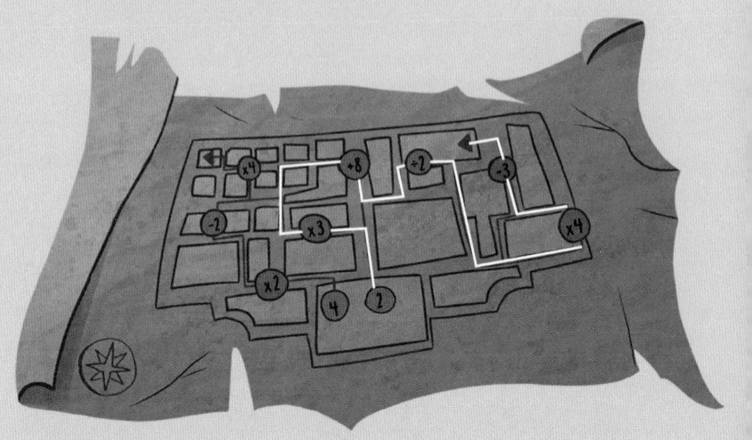

PAGE 18

PAGE 19

$\frac{1}{4}$	30
0.5	62
$5\frac{1}{4}$	82
5.4	$80\frac{1}{2}$
15	80.75
42	

PAGE 20

48

PAGE 21

10

PAGE 22

The scarab gem is numbered
48 (3 x 16).

PAGE 23

44 ÷ 11 = 4
48 ÷ 8 = 6
35 ÷ 7 = 5
27 ÷ 3 = 9
42 ÷ 6 = 7
36 ÷ 12 = 3

PAGE 24

The correct gem is marked
with a white cross.

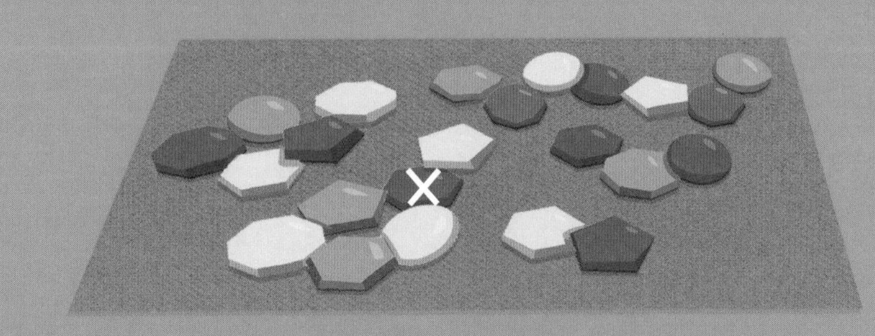

PAGE 25

30% of the gems are blue,
25% are pink, and 40% are oval.

PAGE 26

Pink jewels: 50%,

Blue jewels: 25%,

Yellow jewels: 25%,

Other jewels: 10%.

PAGE 27

Each group needs 1 triangular gem,
1 square gem, 2 circle-shaped gems,
and 5 heart-shaped gems.

PAGE 28

Cleo chooses wand number 9.
34 - 25 = 9.

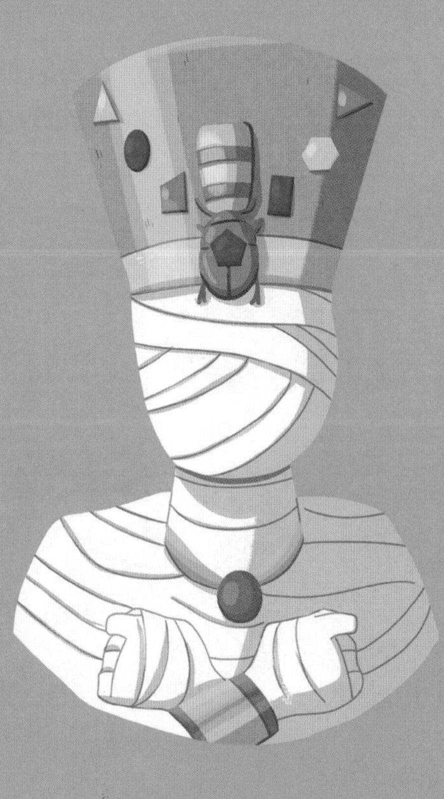

GLOSSARY

CULPRIT The person who is responsible for a crime or misdeed.

DECIMAL A fraction with tenths shown as numbers after a dot, for example $\frac{1}{2} = 0.5$

MILLENNIA A millennium is a period of 1,000 years; millennia are many thousands of years.

PRIME NUMBER A number that can only be divided by itself and 1.

SCARAB An ancient Egyptian gem cut in the shape of a scarab beetle.

VERTICAL Upright—at a 90° angle to something horizontal.

FURTHER INFORMATION

Hore, Rosie and Luana Rinaldo. *Fractions and Decimals Activity Book.* London, UK: Usborne Publishing, 2017.

Tripp, Karyn. *Math Art and Drawing Games for Kids.* Beverly (MA), USA: Quarry Books, 2019.

INDEX